DMITRI KABALEVSKY

(1904-1987)

THIRTY CHILDREN'S PIECES
Opus 27
FOR THE PIANO

Edited by Keith Snell

Kjos NEIL A. KJOS MUSIC COMPANY • PUBLISHER

CONTENTS

For supplementary study, a compact disc recording of Thirty Children's Pieces, Opus 27 *(GP387CD) performed by pianist Diane Hidy, is available from your favorite music dealer. Ms. Hidy's interpretations follow this edition closely as a practical example for students.*

0-8497-9626-1

3

DMITRI KABALEVSKY (1904-1987)

Kabalevsky was born December 30, 1904 in St. Petersburg, Russia. As a young boy he was a musical prodigy. When he was 14, his family moved to Moscow so that he could study piano at the Scriabin Music School. In 1925 he entered the Moscow Conservatory of Music where he studied piano and composition. In 1932, Kabalevsky was appointed Professor of Composition at the Moscow Conservatory.

Developing effective methods for piano teaching was important to Kabalevsky all of his life. In 1962, he was elected head of the Commission of Musical Esthetic Education of Children. In 1959 he became president of the Scientific Council of Educational Esthetics in the Academy of Pedagogical Sciences of the U.S.S.R., and in 1972 he received the honorary degree of President of the International Society of Musical Education.

Famous in Russia for his songs, operas, and cantatas, Kabalevsky is well-known world wide for his many sets of piano pieces. Among the most popular are *Thirty Children's Pieces, Op. 27* and *Twenty-Four Little Pieces, Op. 39*. Throughout both sets Kabalevsky demonstrates his remarkable compositional craft and melodic gift.

Kabalevsky toured many cities in Europe and the United States as a pianist, conductor and composer. He died February 14, 1987 in Moscow.

THIRTY CHILDREN'S PIECES, OPUS 27

The pieces in this collection are an excellent source of intermediate piano literature from the 20th century. They offer a wide variety of musical style and technique.

All pieces in this collection are suitable for recitals, auditions, festivals and contests. The composer did *not* arrange the pieces in this collection in progressive order of difficulty.

The painting on the cover of this book is by Wassily Kandinsky (1866-1944) and is titled *Volga Boat Song* (1906). Kandinsky, a Russian painter, has been credited with creating the first entirely abstract paintings.

GP388

1. WALTZ

Allegretto cantabile

2. SONG

3. ETUDE IN A MINOR

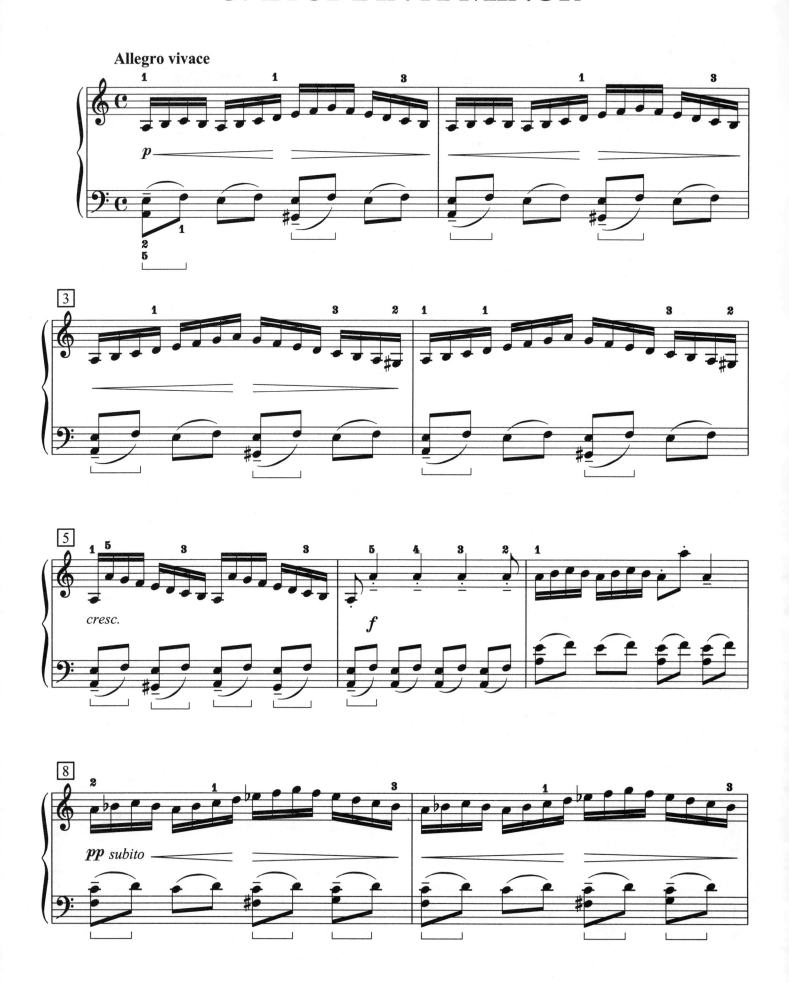

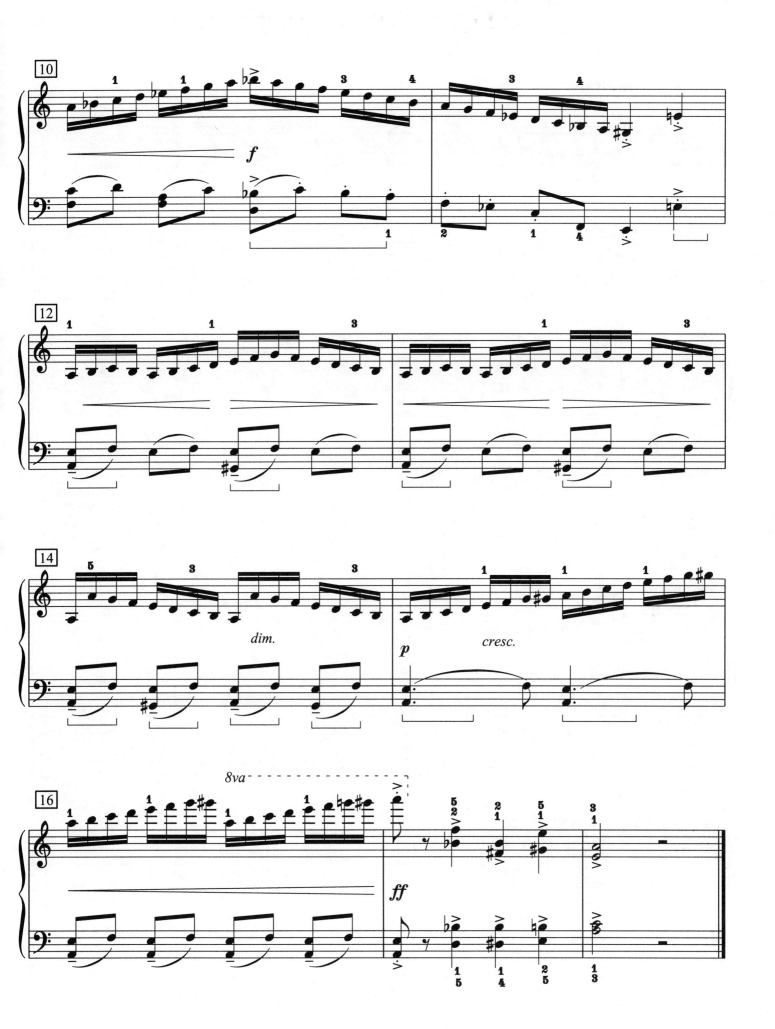

4. NIGHT ON THE RIVER

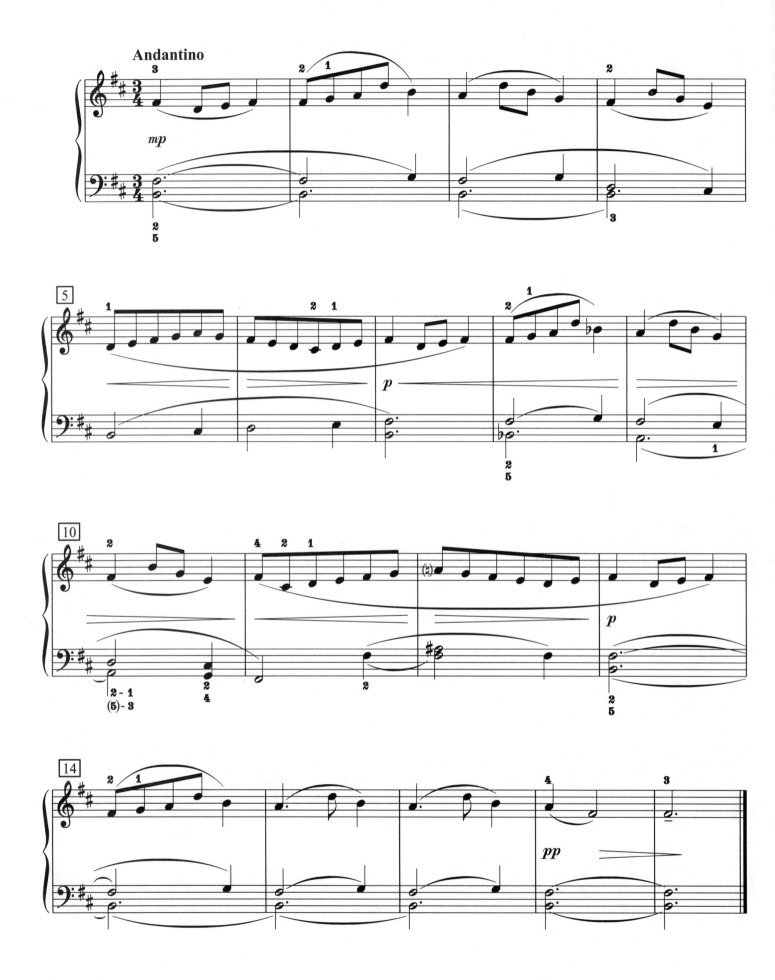

5. PLAYING BALL

6. SAD STORY

7. AN OLD DANCE

Moderato (Tempo di menuetto)

8. LULLABY

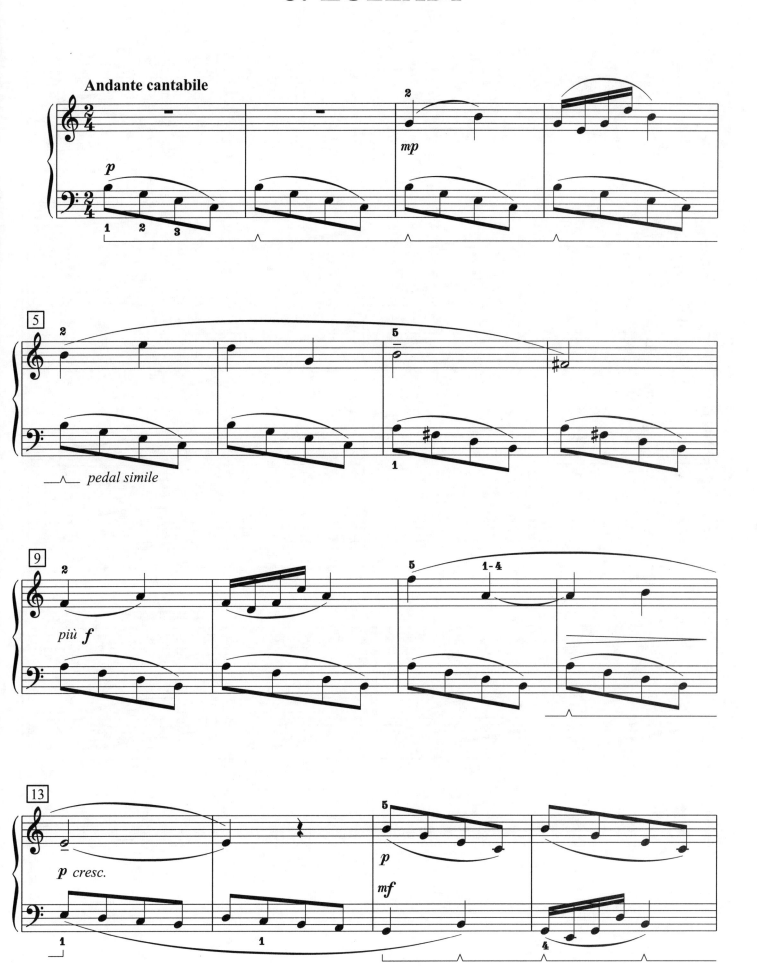

14

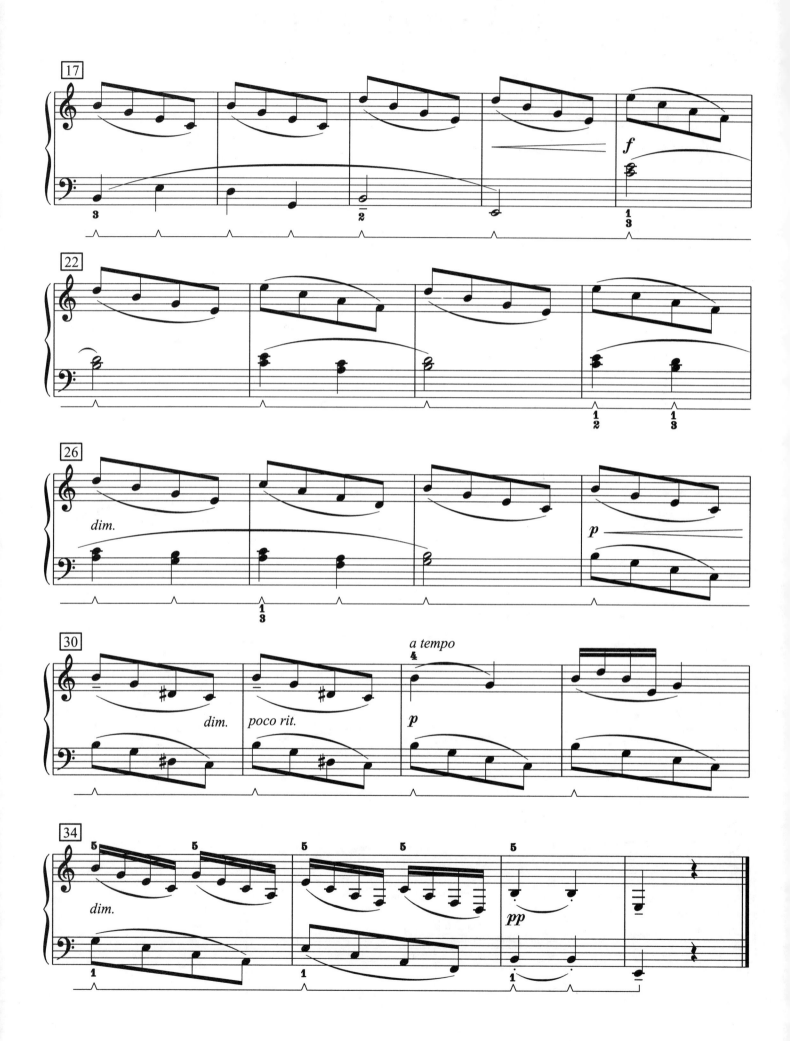

9. A LITTLE FABLE

10. CLOWNING

11. RONDO

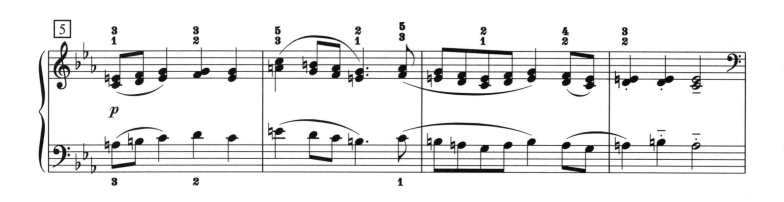

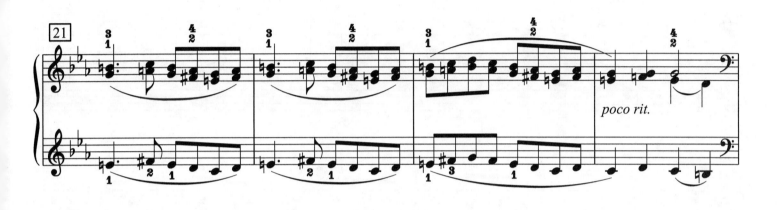

12. Toccatina

13. A LITTLE JOKE

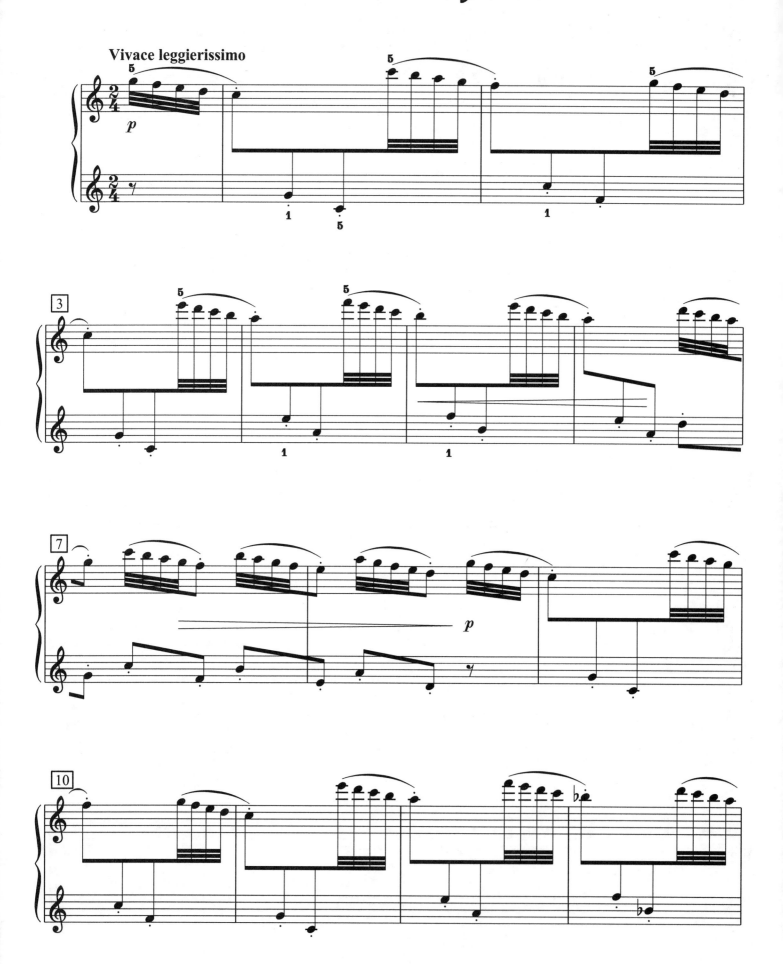

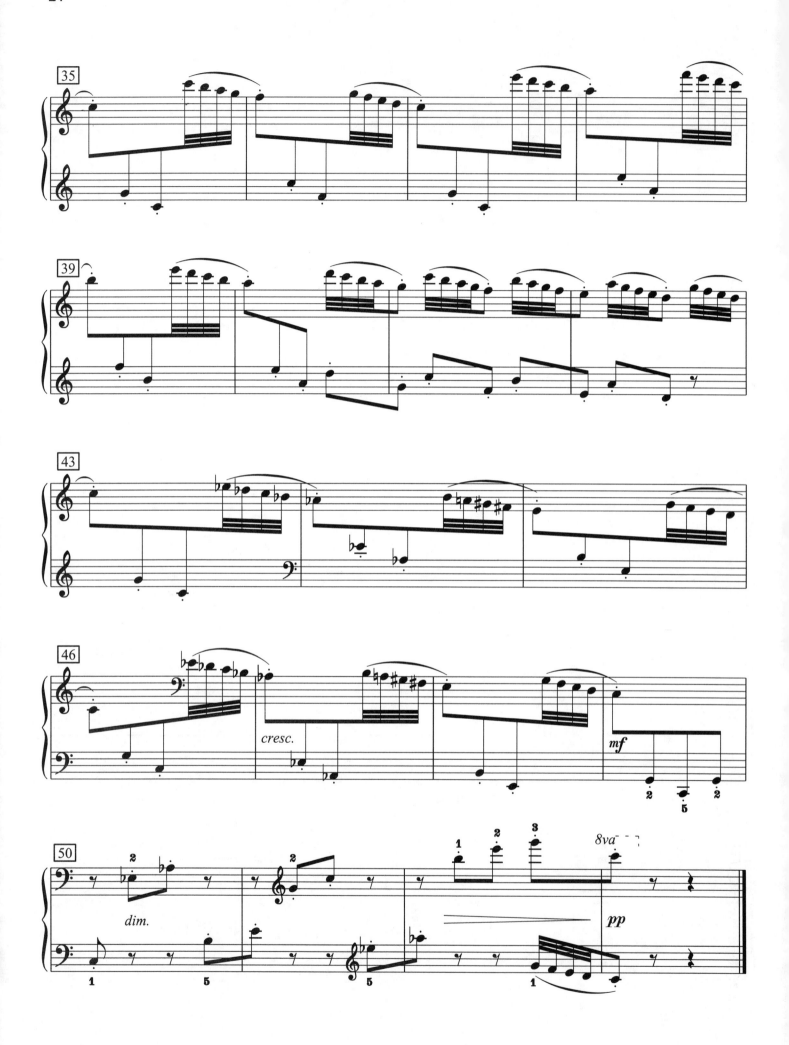

14. Scherzo

15. MARCH

28

GP388

16. Lyrical Piece

30

17. Dance On the Lawn

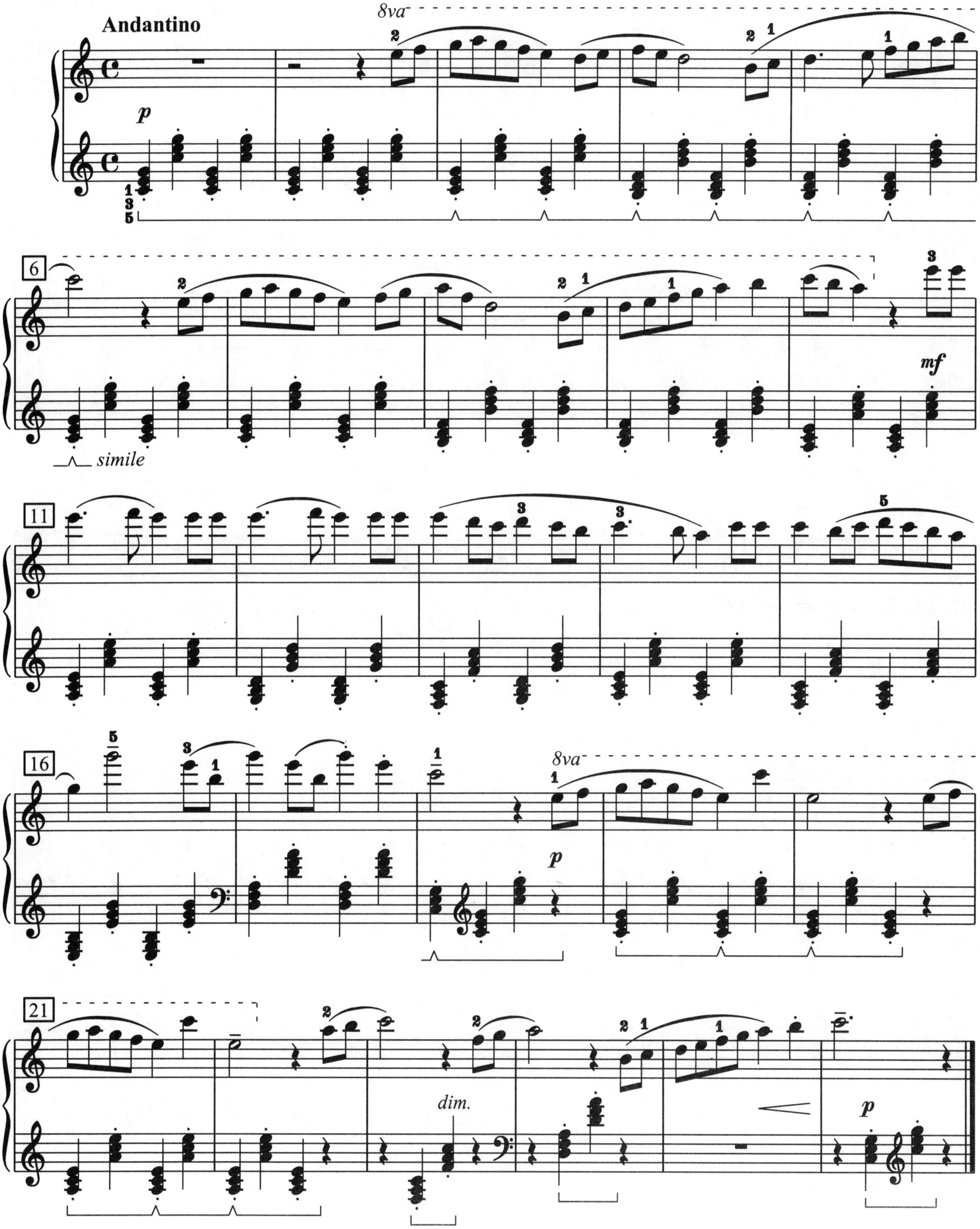

18. SONATINA

19. A WARLIKE DANCE

20. A SHORT STORY

21. THE CHASE

22. A TALE

23. SNOW STORM

44

24. ETUDE IN F MAJOR

46

GP388

25. NOVELETTE

26. ETUDE IN A MAJOR

27. Dance

28. CAPRICE

29. Cavalry Gallop

30. DRAMATIC EVENT